Giant Soup

by Margaret Mahy

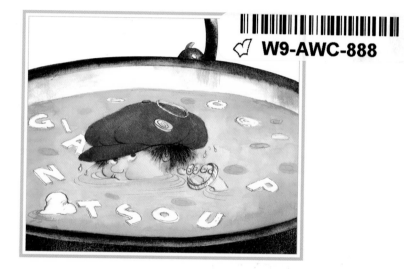

illustrated by Robyn Belton

LEARNING
MEDIA®

The giant's mother
was going on a holiday.
"What shall I eat, Mother?"
asked the giant.

"Make yourself a pot of soup,"
said the giant's mother.

The giant put a big pot of water
on the stove.
He cut up a lot of onions
and put them in the water.
Then he tried it.

"This soup is no good,"
said the giant.
"It must have carrots in it."

The giant went out to his garden
and got some carrots.
He put them into the soup.
Then he tried the soup again.

"This soup is no good,"
said the giant.
"It must have a beef bone in it."

He went to his refrigerator
and got a beef bone.
He put it into the soup.
Then he tried the soup again.

"This soup is still no good,"
said the giant.
"It must have a boy in it."

He put on his giant sneakers
and ran quietly out into the world.
A boy called Jason
was walking home from school.
He was reading a book
as he walked along.
It was a cook book.

The giant came up quietly
behind Jason and caught him.

He took him home
and popped him into
the big pot of soup.

Jason swam round and round
among the bits of onion and carrot.

"Hey!" said Jason.
"You don't know how to cook.
This soup is cold.
Turn on the stove."

The giant turned on the stove.
Jason swam round and round.
He drank a bit of giant soup.

"Hey!" said Jason.
"There's no salt in it.
You can't make soup."

The giant put some salt in the soup.

"That's better," said Jason.
He swam round and round
and drank a bit more soup.

"Don't drink it all!"
cried the giant.

"Hey!" said Jason.
"This soup isn't right.
There's no pepper in it."

The giant put pepper in the soup.
"That's better," said Jason.
The soup was lovely and warm by now.
He swam round and round
among the bits of onion and carrot.
"What lovely soup!" said Jason.

He drank a bit more.

"You're drinking it all!
You're drinking it all!"
cried the giant.
He quickly took Jason out of the soup.
"There will be no soup left for me,"
he said.

"I might as well go home, then,"
said Jason.
"I'll come in tomorrow
and see how you're getting on."

"I'm cooking a cake tomorrow,"
said the giant.

"I'd better come and help you,"
Jason said.
"And I'll bring my cook book."

"Oh, no, no, no!
You eat too much!" cried the giant.
"Don't come back again —
ever, ever, ever!"